Religious Edu and Literacy in the Classroom

Book 1

E. Freedman and J. Keys

Prim-Ed Publishing

www.prim-ed.com

2321 C

Religious Education and Literacy in the Classroom—Book 1
Prim-Ed Publishing

Published in 2004 by Prim-Ed Publishing

Copyright J. Keys and E. Freedman 2004

ISBN 1 86400 787 7
PR–2321

Additional titles available in this series are:
Religious Education and Literacy in the Classroom—Book 2
Religious Education and Literacy in the Classroom—Book 3

Home Page: http://www.prim-ed.com

Prim-Ed Publishing Pty Ltd
Offices in: United Kingdom: PO Box 2840, Coventry, CV6 5ZY   **Email:** sales@prim-ed.com
                Australia: PO Box 332, Greenwood, Western Australia, 6924   **Email:** mail@ricgroup.com.au
                Republic of Ireland: Bosheen, New Ross, Co. Wexford, Ireland   **Email:** sales@prim-ed.com

Internet websites
In some cases, websites or specific URLs may be recommended. While these are checked and rechecked at the time of publication, the
publisher has no control over any subsequent changes which may be made to webpages. It is *strongly* recommended that the class teacher
checks *all* URLs before allowing students to access them.

Foreword

RE and Literacy in the Classroom is a three-book series written to help schools meet the requirements of Religious Education in the classroom. It sits easily beside the non-statutory national expectations and the QCA scheme of work.

RE teaching is most effective when it includes both learning about religion (AT1) and learning from religion (AT2). Therefore, each six–page unit of work includes one activity from each attainment target, covering:

- knowledge and understanding of religious beliefs and teachings; religious practices and lifestyles and ways of expressing meaning;
- the skill of asking and responding to questions of identity and experience; meaning and purpose and values and commitments.

This will help children to learn about Christianity and the other principal religions, as well as develop their ability to think about and respond to what they have learnt.

Each book contains a selection of the world's greatest sacred stories from different faiths.

Each unit is based upon one of these sacred stories, retold through text and pictures. The accompanying activities include an exploration of the different faiths and their beliefs with an underpinning of good literacy practice. This brings language and communication into partnership with RE. The literacy opportunities in each unit include:

- a sacred story for discussion and study;
- presentation of their own ideas using different writing genres; and
- a relevant word or text level activity from the Literacy Strategy scheme of work.

The accompanying comprehensive teachers notes provide curriculum links, story references, discussion points, resource lists and answers.

The three books in this series are:

RE and Literacy in the Classroom Book 1 (Ages 5–7)
RE and Literacy in the Classroom Book 2 (Ages 7–9)
RE and Literacy in the Classroom Book 3 (Ages 9–11)

Contents

Teachers Notes

Each six-page unit of work starts with two pages of comprehensive teachers notes. The information provided in these teachers notes includes:

The religion from which the sacred story is derived.

Table of curriculum links to show how the activities fit into the following curricular requirements for Year R/1/2 pupils:

- RE Non-statutory Guidance
- RE QCA Scheme of Work
- National Literacy Strategy

The story reference has been included for teachers wishing to do further work on the sacred story.

The second (RE AT1), third (RE AT2) and fourth (Literacy Strategy) copymasters are explained in further detail. The teachers notes on these activities may include some of the following:

- preparation
- introduction
- discussion
- additional/extension activities
- resources
- answers.

Introductory activities and discussion points based on the sacred story.

The first copymaster in each unit is a sacred story from one of the major faiths. The stories are retold through text and pictures. Teachers can use the stories in a variety of ways to suit their own routines and the age and ability of their class. The story may be read aloud to the class or group by the teacher or may be distributed to children to read individually, in pairs or in small groups. Children will often benefit from having their own copy of the text to refer to when completing the subsequent activities. Alternatively, teachers could display the story page on an overhead projector for the class, use a single enlarged photocopy for group reading, or make a few photocopies and laminate them as a permanent resource for the class. The stories could also be used as the basis for an assembly.

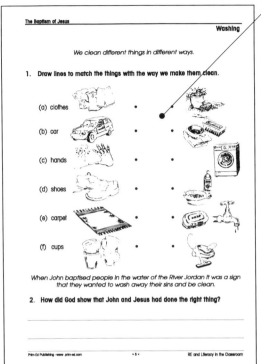

The second copymaster in each unit is an activity based on the AT1 non-statutory guidelines in RE. Children will be asked to recount or retell the stories. This covers learning about religions, showing knowledge and understanding of what people believe, what they do and how they express their beliefs. This page may be used as either part of a specific RE lesson or as a text-level activity during the Literacy Hour.

The third copymaster in each unit is intended to stimulate discussion based around the requirements of the AT2 non-statutory guidelines in RE. Children are encouraged to respond to stories from different religions by relating them to their own life and experience. They will compare aspects of their own experience with those of others.

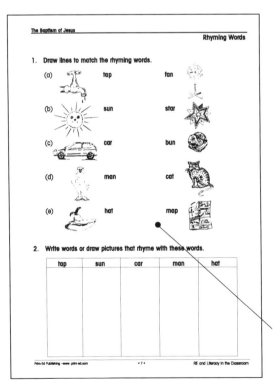

The fourth and final copymaster in each unit offers a variety of Literacy Strategy independent word and text-level work, all based on the sacred story.

Page iv contains religion–based merit certificates. These can be photocopied onto coloured paper or card and given to children to encourage them to try their best and promote their self-esteem. These certificates will also help to provide a positive working environment.

Pages v–xi include graphics from the major faiths covered in this series, to be used as clip art, to complement your teaching programme. They have a multitude of uses including display and pupil and teacher reference.

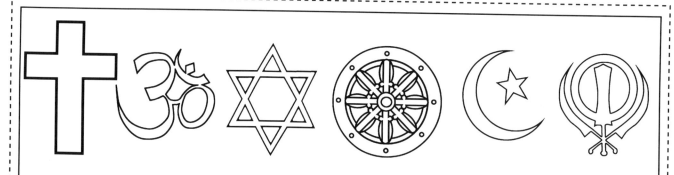

Great R. E. Work!

Name: _____

Date: _____ Signed: _____

Super Effort!

Name: _____

Awarded for:

Signed: _____

Date: _____

Star R.E. Pupil

Name: _____

Signed: _____

Date: _____

Christianity Clip Art

Judaism Clip Art

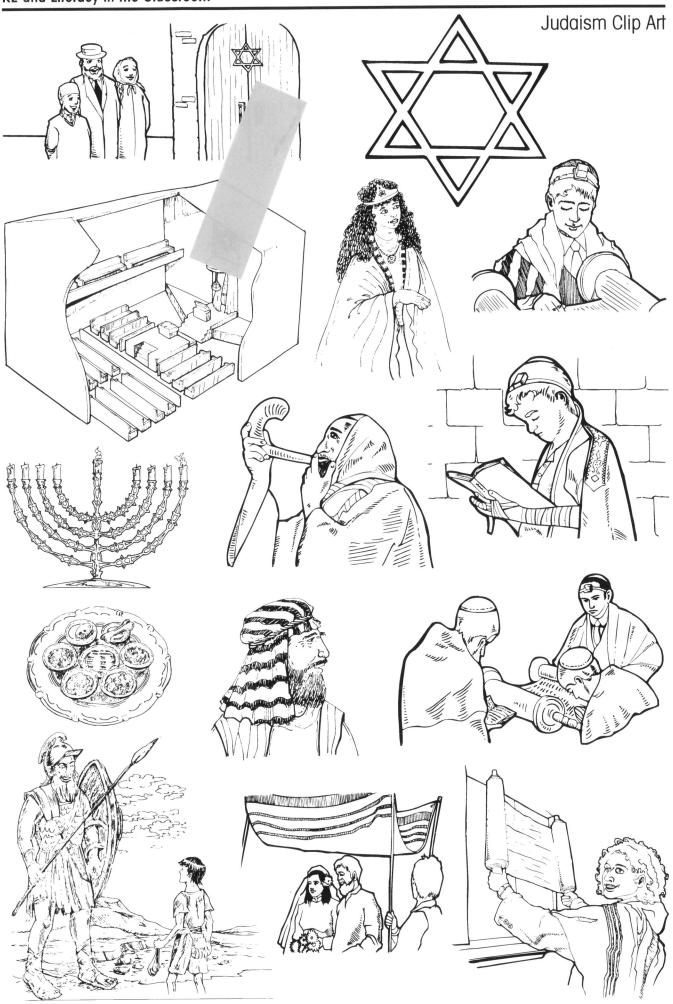

Hinduism Clip Art

Sikhism Clip Art

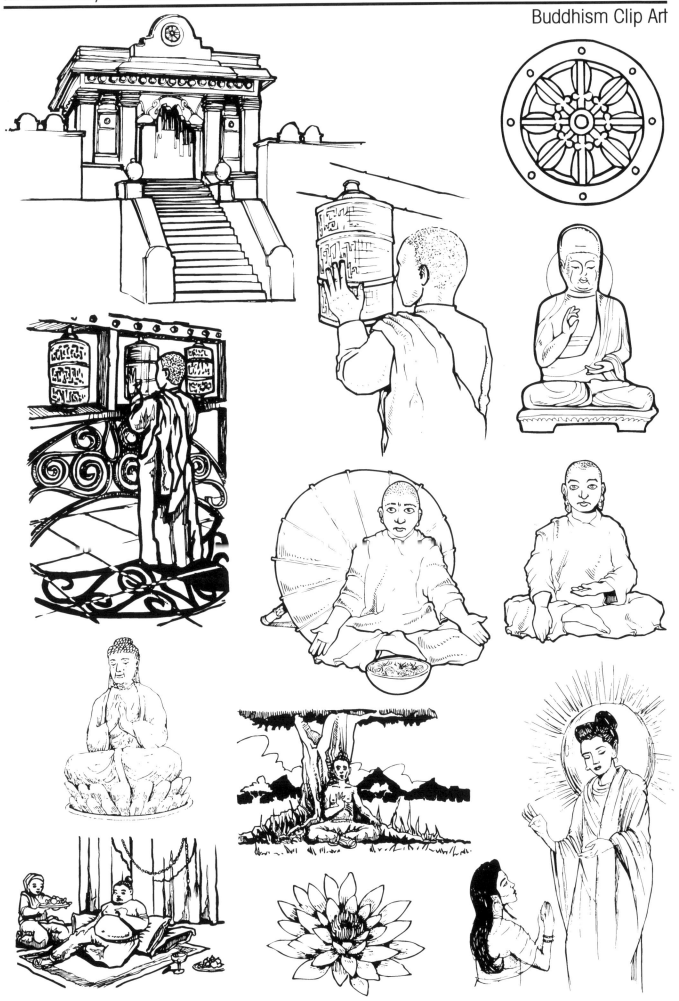

Teachers Notes

Religion: Christianity

Curriculum Links:

R.E. Attainment Target 1: Learning about Religions
- Beliefs and teachings - recount outlines of some religious stories.
- Practices and lifestyles - recognise features of religious life and practice.

R.E. Attainment Target 2: Learning from Religion
- Identify and experience - identify aspects of own experience and feelings in religious material studied.

QCA R.E. Scheme of Work Reference
- 1B - What does it mean to belong in Christianity?

National Literacy Strategy Reference
- Year 1, Term 1, Word 5 - rhyming CVC words.

Story Reference:
The Bible: New Testament, Matthew Chapter 3; Mark Chapter 1; Luke Chapter 3 and John Chapter 1.

Notes – Page 4 – The Story of the Baptism of Jesus:

Introduction:
- Read the story with the children.
- Ask the children if they can retell the story in their own words.
- Discuss what they can see happening in the pictures.
- Children can colour their own copy of the story to keep.

Discussion:
- What relation was John to Jesus?
- Why does John encourage people to be baptised?
- Who does John say is coming?
- Why does John say that it should be Jesus who baptises him?
- Whose voice comes from heaven?

Notes – Page 5 – Washing:

Introduction/Discussion:
Washing:
- Why is it important for people to wash?
- What things can we use to wash ourselves with? Class brainstorm and write a list on board; e.g. shampoo, flannel.
- Why is it important to wash some things around us?
- What are the things around us that we need to wash; e.g. clothes, plates?
- What do we use to wash these things with e.g. washing powder, washing-up liquid?
- Show children a selection of washing/cleaning materials. What would each of them be used to clean? e.g. shampoo (hair), duster (furniture), disinfectant (toilet).

Baptism:
- Why is water used to baptise people?
- Was God happy or sad that John baptised Jesus?

Resources:
- A collection of washing products; e.g. shampoo, soap, washing up liquid (or magazine pictures of these products).
- Pencil or pen, crayons and ruler.

Answers:
1. clothes – washing machine.
   car – hose, bucket, sponge.
   hands – soap, water.
   shoes – shoe polish, cloth.
   carpet – vacuum cleaner.
   cups – water, detergent.
2. God sent a dove down from heaven and said He was pleased with Jesus.

Notes – Page 6 – Celebrating a New Baby:

Preparation:
- In preparation for this activity, children will need to talk to members of their family about how their own birth was celebrated. The children could bring in photographs of their christening or equivalent ceremony. Alternatively, some children could report on recent experience of the birth of siblings.

Discussion:
- Children tell class how their family celebrated their birth or that of their siblings, before recording the information on the worksheet.

Resources:
- Pencil or pen and crayons.

Answers:
- Teacher check.

Notes – Page 7 – Rhyming Words:

Extension:
- Discuss/List words which rhyme with other CVC words.

Resources:
- Pencil or pen, crayons, scissors and glue.

Answers:
Column 2 – map, bun, star, fan, cat.
Column 3 – Teacher check.

The Story of the Baptism of Jesus

John was a cousin of Jesus. He preached to the people. He said they should get ready for someone who was coming soon. John baptised the people in the River Jordan.

Jesus asked John to baptise him.

John replied, 'I should be baptised by you, and yet you have come to me'.

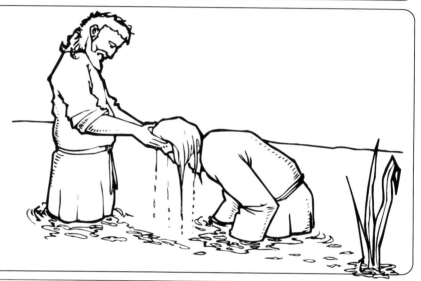

A voice from heaven said, 'This is my own dear son and I am pleased with Him'.

You will find this story in all four Gospels of the Bible:
Matthew Chapter 3, Mark Chapter 1, Luke Chapter 3 and John Chapter 1.

We clean different things in different ways.

1. Draw lines to match the things with the way we make them clean.

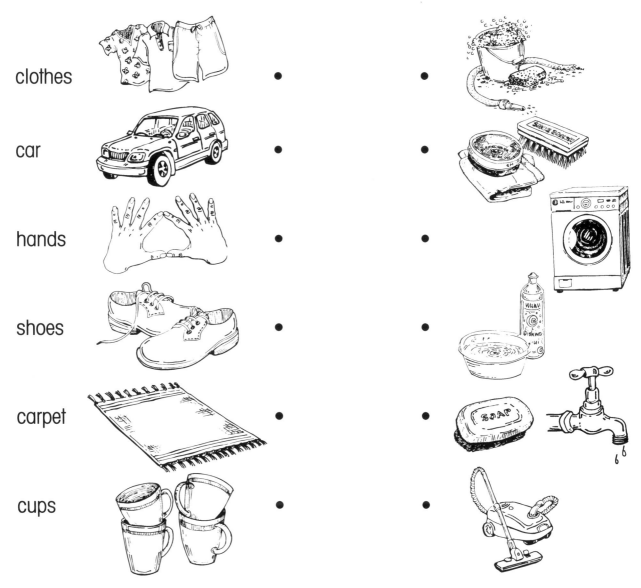

clothes

car

hands

shoes

carpet

cups

When John baptised people in the water of the River Jordan it was a sign that they wanted to wash away their sins and be clean.

2. How did God show that John and Jesus had done the right thing?

_____

_____

Celebrating a New Baby

When a new baby is born, the family will celebrate.

1. **Ask your family if they did anything special when you were born.**

2. **Write about what your family did to celebrate your birth.**

When I was born_____

_____

_____

_____

_____

_____

_____

3. **Draw a picture of yourself as a baby.**

Rhyming Words

Look at each picture.	Stick a rhyming word picture.	Write or draw more rhyming words.

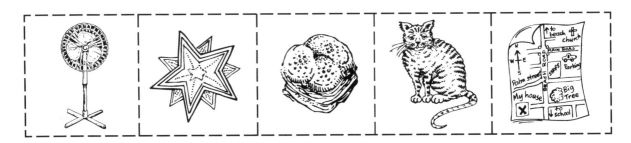

Teachers Notes

Religion: Christianity

Curriculum Links:

R.E. Attainment Target 1: Learning about Religions

- Beliefs and teachings - retell religious stories.
- Expression and language - suggest meanings in stories.

R.E. Attainment Target 2: Learning from Religion

- Identify and experience - respond sensitively to the experiences and feelings of others.

QCA R.E. Scheme of Work Reference

- 2B - Why did Jesus tell stories?

National Literacy Strategy Reference

- Year 2, Term 3, Text 10 - writing sustained stories.

Story Reference:

The Bible: New Testament, Luke Chapter 15.

Notes – Page 10 – The Story of the Prodigal Son:

Introduction:
- Read the story with the children.
- Discuss any unfamiliar vocabulary.

Discussion:
- Remind children that this is a story Jesus told his friends in order to teach them something.
- What do the class think is the message of this story?
- Who does the father in the story represent?
- People who try to be good Christians are like which of the brothers?
- Does Jesus say it is too late for the brother who went away to become a member of the family again?
- Children could act out the story in small groups.

Notes – Page 11 – What are they Thinking?:

Introduction/Discussion:
- Children need to look carefully at the pictures of the three characters from the story and decide who they are.
- Read the speech bubbles with the children and discuss which story character will feel like this.

Resources:
- Crayons, scissors, glue and paper.

Answers:
- Prodigal son - 'I went off to have a good time ...'
- Father - 'My younger son had been gone for a long time ...'
- Older brother - 'It's not fair ...'

Notes – Page 12 – Feelings:

Introduction/Discussion:
- Children look at the illustrations and identify the story characters.
- Ask children to suggest appropriate words and phrases to describe the feelings of each story character.
- Write keywords on the board for children to use in their own sentences.

Resources:
- Pencil or pen and crayons.

Answers:
- Picture 1: Prodigal son – excited, happy, thrilled, pleased, rich etc.
- Picture 2: Prodigal son – poor, sad, hungry, lonely etc.
- Picture 3: Father – surprised, loving, excited, happy etc.
- Picture 4: Older brother – sad, jealous, upset, miserable, left out etc.

Notes – Page 13 – A Story that Jesus Told:

Introduction:
- Explain to the children that the Gospels include many stories called parables that Jesus told as a way of preaching to his followers.
- Read the children one or more parables.
- Children retell their chosen parables orally in their own words before writing their parable onto the copymaster.

Suitable Parables:
- The Good Samaritan – Luke, Chapter 10.
- The Rich Man's Feast – Luke, Chapter 14.
- The Lost Sheep – Matthew, Chapter 18 and Luke, Chapter 15.
- The Two House Builders – Matthew, Chapter 7.

Resources:
- Bible, pencil or pen and crayons.

Answers:
- Teacher check.

The Story of the Prodigal Son

This is a story that Jesus told. He wanted to show His disciples how much God loves us and how pleased He is if we repent and come back to Him.

There was once a man who had two sons. The younger son asked his father for his share of the money and went to live in a country far away. There he lived foolishly, and spent all his money enjoying himself.

He had to get a job looking after pigs, and he got so hungry he wished he could eat the bean pods that the pigs ate. He realised that even the hired workers on his father's farm lived better than this, so he decided to go home and ask for work, since he did not think he deserved to be treated as a son of the house any more.

He was still a long way from home when his father saw him and ran to give him a hug. The son said that he was sorry and his father called the servants to prepare a feast.

In the meantime the older brother was working in the fields. When he came back and heard what was happening he was angry and would not come inside. He said that they had never had a feast like that for him, although he had worked hard on the farm for years.

His father went outside to him and explained;

'My son, you are always here with me, and everything I have is yours. But we had to celebrate and be happy, because your brother was dead, but now he is alive; he was lost, but now he has been found.'

Jesus told this story two thousand years ago but we can still understand the feelings of the father and the two brothers.

Jesus often made up stories like these for His followers. They are called parables.
You will find this parable in the Gospel of St Luke, Chapter 15. We can enjoy listening to them as stories, but they also teach us important lessons.

What are they Thinking?

1. Read the speech bubbles, colour the pictures and cut them out.

2. Match each picture to a bubble. Glue the pairs onto paper.

My younger son had been gone for a long time and I missed him very much. I am so happy he has come home, we're going to celebrate with a special family meal together.

It's not fair! I've been working on the farm all these years. Dad never lets me have a treat with my friends. Now my brother's come home and there's all this fuss.

I went off to have a good time. When the money ran out I got a job looking after pigs. But the pigs were eating better than I was, so I came home and asked for a job on the family farm.

Write one sentence to say how the main character in each picture is feeling.

A Story that Jesus Told

Religion: Christianity/Judaism

Curriculum Links:

R.E. Attainment Target 1: Learning about Religions • Beliefs and teachings - recount outlines of some religious stories.
R.E. Attainment Target 2: Learning from Religion • Meaning and purpose - identify things they find interesting or puzzling in religious materials studied.
QCA R.E. Scheme of Work Reference • RC - Who was Noah?
National Literacy Strategy Reference • Year R, Text 1 - recognise printed words, e.g. on labels.

Story Reference:

The Bible: Old Testament, Genesis Chapters 6 – 8.

Notes – Page 16 – The Story of Noah:

Introduction:

- Show the children the cartoon story.
- Discuss what happens when there is a flood.
- Tell the story of Noah from the book of Genesis, or an appropriate children's version of the story.

Discussion:

- Ask the children to describe what is happening in each picture.
- Discuss how Noah and his family built the ark.
- How did Noah feel when the rain came?
- What happened after the water went down?
- How did Noah and the animals feel after the flood?

Notes – Page 17 – The End of the Flood:

Introduction/Discussion:

- Remind the children how Noah found out if the flood water had gone down by sending first a raven and then a dove. The raven did not return, but the dove came back because it could find nowhere dry to perch. The next time Noah sent the dove it found an olive tree and flew back with a small branch, so Noah knew the trees were now above the water. Next time Noah sent the dove it did not come back, so Noah knew there was dry land.
- Discuss how Noah and his family might have felt when the dove came back with the olive branch.

Resources:

- Pencil or pen and crayons.

Answers:

- Teacher check.

Notes – Page 18 – A Rainbow:

Introduction:

- Tell the children about the rainbow that God sent after the flood. Read them the sentence about God's promise.
- Show the children a photograph or drawing of a rainbow. Discuss the excitement of seeing a rainbow in the sky.
- Read the colour words on the rainbow. Check that the children can read and identify all of the colours correctly.

Resources:

- Bible, photograph or picture of a rainbow, pencil or pen and crayons.

Answers:

- Teacher check.

Notes – Page 19 – Animals:

Introduction:

- Look at the animal pictures with the children.
- Ensure that children know the names of the animals and can read the name labels.
- Discuss which animal pairs look the same and which ones look very different.

Resources:

- Scissors, glue, crayons and paper.

Answers:

- Lion and lioness.
- Bull and cow.
- Stag and doe.
- Peacock and peahen.
- Ram and ewe.

The End of the Flood

How did Noah see that the flood was over?

_____

_____

_____

_____

A Rainbow

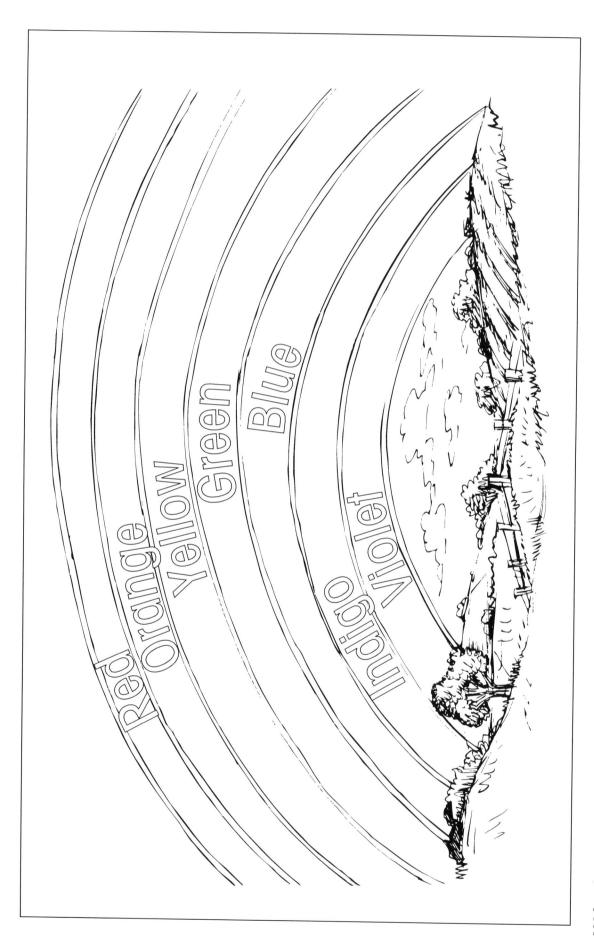

Red Orange Yellow Green Blue Indigo Violet

Write how you feel when you see a rainbow.

Colour and cut out the animals. Glue each animal next to its partner.

peacock

stag

ram

peahen

bull

lion

cow

doe

lioness

ewe

Religion: Christianity

Curriculum Links:

R.E. Attainment Target 1: Learning about Religions
• Beliefs and teachings - recount outlines of some religious stories.

R.E. Attainment Target 2: Learning from Religion
• Values and commitments - identify what is of value and concern to themselves in religious material studied.

QCA R.E. Scheme of Work Reference
• RB - Who were the friends of Jesus?

National Literacy Strategy Reference
• Year R, Word 2 - hear and identify initial sounds in words.

Story Reference:

The Bible: New Testament, Luke Chapter 19, Verses 1 – 10.
Scriptures quoted from *The Good News Bible*
(The Bible Societies/Harper Collins Publishers, 1966, 1971, 1976 and 1992).

Notes – Page 22 – The Story of Zacchaeus:

Introduction/Discussion:
- Read the Bible story to the children.
- Discuss any unfamiliar vocabulary.
- Explore how Zacchaeus must have felt at the end of the story.
- Discuss the things that we do for our friends.

Notes – Page 23 – A Friend of Jesus:

Introduction/Discussion:
- Remind the children of the sequence of events in the story of Zacchaeus.
- Look closely at the pictures with the children.
- Ask the children to colour and cut out the pictures and glue them in the correct order.

Resources:
- Crayons, scissors, glue and paper.

Answers:
1. Illustration with speech: 'Why is he collecting money for the Romans?'
2. Illustration with speech: 'Jesus is coming!'
3. Illustration with speech: 'I am coming to your house!'
4. Illustration with speech: 'I promise to help the poor.'

Notes – Page 24 – What is a Friend?:

Introduction/Discussion:
- Discuss friendship and children's expectations of how a friend will behave in various situations.
- Look at the pictures on the worksheet and discuss what is happening in each picture.
- Ask the children to decide which of the children is acting like a true friend.

Resources:
- Pencil or pen and crayons.

Answers:
1. The following pictures should be coloured:
- child helping other child who has fallen over;
- child offering other hot child a glass of water;
- child with arm around other child who is crying; and
- child sharing chocolate with other child.
2. Teacher check.

Notes – Page 25 – A Special Word:

Introduction/Discussion:
- Explain to the children that they need to look at each picture in turn, sound out the word and write down the first letter. This will then give the children a new word to write.

Resources:
- Pencil or pen and crayons.

Answers:
- F R I E N D S

The Story of Zacchaeus

Jesus was passing through Jericho. There was a chief tax collector there named Zacchaeus, who was rich. He was trying to see who Jesus was, but he was a little man and could not see Jesus because of the crowd. So he ran ahead of the crowd and climbed a sycamore tree to see Jesus, who was going to pass that way.

When Jesus came to that place, he looked up and said to Zacchaeus,

'Hurry down, Zacchaeus, because I must stay in your house today'.

Zacchaeus hurried down and welcomed him with great joy. All the people who saw it started grumbling,

'This man has gone as a guest to the home of a sinner!' Zacchaeus stood up and said to the Lord,

'Listen, sir! I will give half my belongings to the poor, and if I have cheated anyone, I will pay back four times as much'.

Jesus said to him,

'Salvation has come to this house today, for this man, also, is a descendant of Abraham. The Son of Man came to seek and to save the lost'.

© The Good News Bible.

A Friend of Jesus

What is a Friend?

1. **Look at the pictures. Colour the pictures where you can see someone being a good friend.**

2. **Write another way you can be a good friend.**

_____

_____

_____

1. **Write the first letter of each word.**

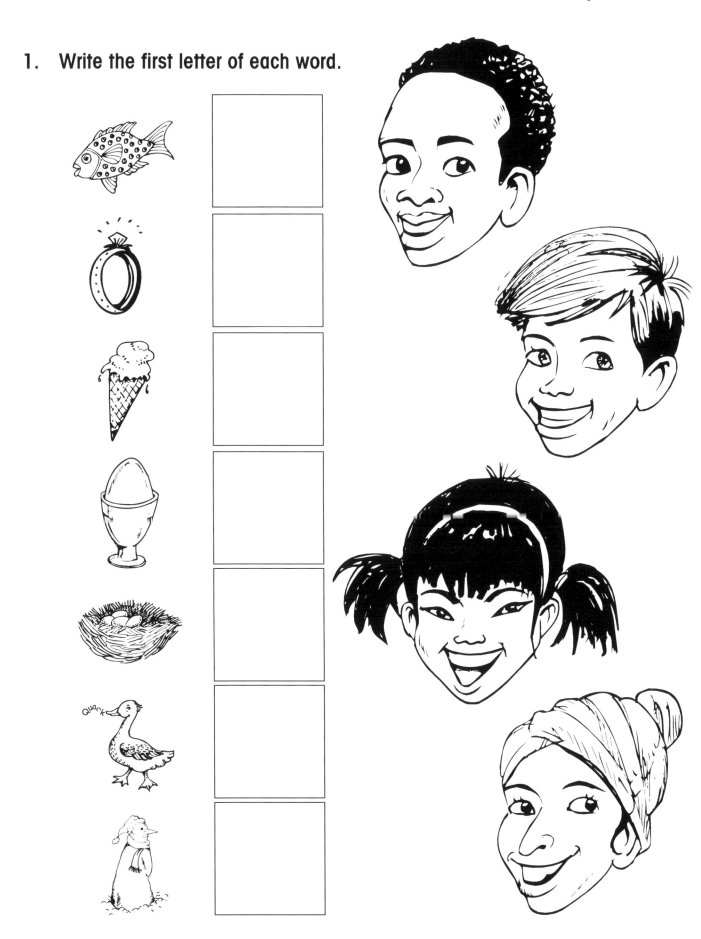

2. **What word did you find?**_____

Teachers Notes

Religion: Christianity

Curriculum Links:

R.E. Attainment Target 1: Learning about Religions
- Beliefs and teachings - retell religious stories.
- Expression and language - suggest meanings in stories.

R.E. Attainment Target 2: Learning from Religion
- Values and commitments - make links between values and commitments, including religious ones, and their own attitudes or behaviour.

QCA R.E. Scheme of Work Reference
- 1D - Beliefs and practice.
- 2B - Why did Jesus tell stories?

National Literacy Strategy Reference
- Year 1, Term 2, Word 2 and 3 - words ending in -ck and -nd.

Story Reference:

The Bible: New Testament, Matthew Chapter 7 and Luke Chapter 6.

Notes – Page 28 – The Parable of the Two Builders:

Introduction/Discussion:
- Read the story with the children.
- Look at the illustrations and discuss what is happening.
- What kind of foundations do modern houses have? Why?
- Jesus said that anyone who heard what He said and obeyed His teachings was like the wise man, and people who listened to Jesus but did not follow Him were like the foolish man.
- Children may be familiar with the song 'The Wise Man Built his House upon a Rock', which is based on this parable, and often sung in school assemblies.

Notes – Page 29 – Our House:

Introduction/Discussion:
- Read the text with the children.
- Ask children to imagine that they are members of one of the families in the story.
- Complete the writing frame to retell the story of the wise or the foolish builder.

Resources:
- Pencil or pen.

Answers:
- Teacher check.

Notes – Page 30 – Adjectives:

Introduction/Discussion:
- Offer the children the opportunity to feel the texture of sand and rock.
- Discuss how the textures differ.
- Read the activity sheet together.
- Define what an adjective is.
- Brainstorm appropriate adjectives for the four sections of the worksheet.

Resources:
Sand, rock, pencil or pen and crayons.

Answers:
- Teacher check - answers could include:
  Sand: yellow, soft, gritty, weak, fluid etc.
  Rock: various colour words, hard, strong, solid, firm etc.
  Man who built on sand: foolish, silly, wrong etc.
  Man who built on rock: sensible, wise, clever, intelligent etc.

Notes – Page 31 – Rhyming Words:

Introduction/Discussion:
- Look at the worksheet with the children - ensure they can identify all of the objects in the illustrations.
- Encourage the children to sound out the names of the objects and listen to the word endings.

Resources:
- Pencil or pen and brown and yellow crayons.

Answers:
- Colour brown: clock, sock, lock, building block, flock of sheep.
- Colour yellow: hand, hair band, land.

The Two Builders

Once upon a time there were two men, who each wanted to build a fine house for their families.

One man built his house on rock, and the other man built his house on sand.

All summer they lived happily in their new houses. However, when winter came, the wind blew and the rain poured down. The river flooded. The house on the rock stood firm, but the house on the sand fell down.

• 28 •

Our House

Imagine your father was one of the builders in the story. Complete the sentences.

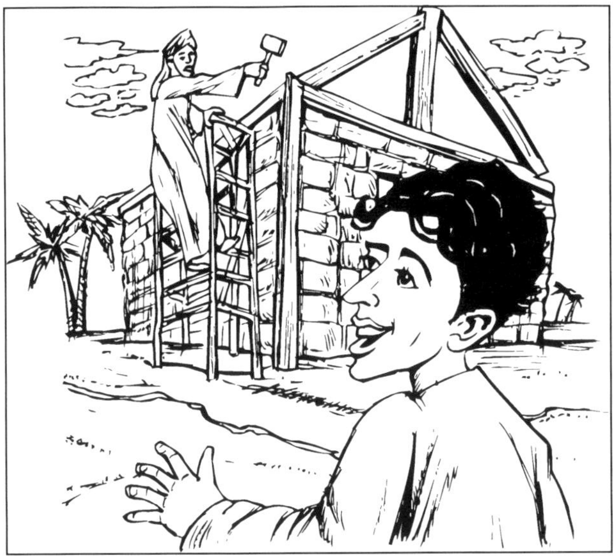

When my dad built the house ...

In the summer ...

When winter came ...

When I grow up and build a house ...

Adjectives are words we use to describe people and objects.

Use adjectives to complete the sentences.

Sand is

_____

_____

_____

_____

Rock is

_____

_____

_____

_____

The man who built his
house on the sand was

_____

_____

_____

_____

The man who built his
house on the rock was

_____

_____

_____

_____

Jesus told his followers that anyone who heard his words and obeyed them was
like the man who built on rock. Those who heard his words but did not obey were
like the man who built on sand.

Rhyming Words

Each of the words below rhymes with rock or sand.

1. Colour the objects that rhyme with rock brown.

2. Colour the objects that rhyme with sand yellow.

3. Write each word underneath.

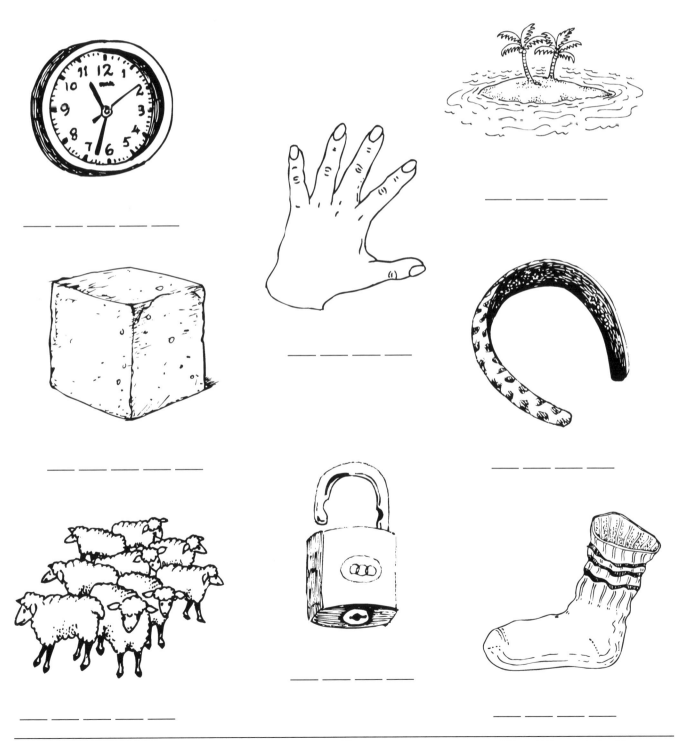

Religion: Judaism

Curriculum Links:

R.E. Attainment Target 1: Learning about Religions
- Beliefs and teachings - retell religious stories.
- Practices and lifestyle - recognise features of religious life and practice.

R.E. Attainment Target 2: Learning from Religion
- Identity and experience - identify aspects of own experience and feelings in religious materials studied.
- Values and commitments - making sense of right and wrong.

QCA R.E. Scheme of Work Reference
- 2C - Celebrations.
- 1E - How do Jewish people express their beliefs?

National Literacy Strategy Reference
- Year 2, Term 3, Word 9 - vocabulary extension and words linked to particular topics.

Story Reference:

The Bible: Old Testament, Esther, Chapters 3 – 9.

Seasonal Link:

The festival of Purim is celebrated during February. The exact date in our calendar will vary from year to year.

Notes – Page 34 – The Story of Queen Esther:

Introduction/Discussion:
- The story of Esther is known as the Megillah and is always read in the synagogue in the evening at the beginning of Purim.
- Read the story to the children.
- Explain any unfamiliar words.
- Why didn't Haman like Mordecai?
- Why did Mordecai think Esther could help them?
- What did Esther do?
- What happened to Haman? Was this fair?
- Why is the festival called Purim?
- Why do Jews celebrate at Purim?

Notes – Page 35 – The Festival of Purim:

Introduction/Discussion:
- Read the text with the children.
- Discuss the information about how Purim is celebrated.
- Can the children think of other happy festivals they have experienced?

Additional Activities:
- Have a Purim party at school. Children can wear fancy dress and sample the special sweet Purim pastries called Haman's Ears. Read the children the story of Esther from page 34 and encourage them to respond to the names with cheers and boos.

Resources:
- Pencil or pen and crayons.

Answers:
2. Esther - hooray!
   Haman - boo!
   Mordecai - hooray!
3. Wear - fancy dress/anything we like.
   Eat - Haman's Ears/special pastries.
   Other festival foods - teacher check.

Notes – Page 36 – My Purim Clothes:

Introduction/Discussion:
- Discuss with the children the kind of clothes they would normally wear to attend a religious service.
- Show illustrations of Orthodox Jewish children. Girls will be modestly dressed with long sleeves and skirts, boys will wear a small hat called a kippah.
- Compare these outfits with the fancy dress permitted at Purim.
- Ask the children what the normal rules are for listening during Bible readings in assembly/church/synagogue.
- Compare these with the rattles, hooters, stamping and shouting allowed at Purim.
- What does this tell us about the atmosphere in the synagogue at Purim?

Resources:
- Pencil or pen, crayons and non-fiction books containing pictures of traditional Orthodox Jewish dress.

Answers:
- Teacher check.

Notes – Page 37 – Festivals:

Introduction/Discussion:
- Discuss religious festivals the children have learned about; e.g. Purim, Christmas, Diwali etc.
- List other Jewish religious festivals; e.g. Passover, Sukkot, Hanukkah.
- Look in non-fiction books to research more about these festivals.

Resources:
- Pencil or pen and crayons.

Answers:
- festivals, Purim, Esther, Passover, bread, leaves, Sukkot, candles, Hanukkah.

The Story of Queen Esther

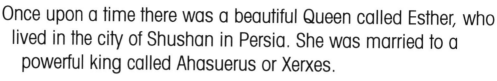

Once upon a time there was a beautiful Queen called Esther, who lived in the city of Shushan in Persia. She was married to a powerful king called Ahasuerus or Xerxes.

In that city there was a man called Haman who worked for the king. He thought he was very important. He wanted everyone to bow to him, and everyone did, except Esther's father, Mordecai.

'I only bow to my God,' said Mordecai.

Haman didn't like this, so he went to the king and complained about Mordecai and the other Jews, saying that they did not show enough respect to Haman or to the king.

'What shall we do?' asked the king.

'We should kill the Jews,' said Haman.

So they decided to cast lots (called Purim) to choose a day when all the Jews in Persia would be killed.

Of course, all the Jews were very worried. Mordecai went to ask his daughter, Queen Esther, to make the king change his mind.

'I can't,' said Esther.

'But you must,' said Mordecai, 'you're the queen.'

So Queen Esther invited King Ahasuerus and Haman to come to dinner with her the next day. It was a fantastic meal, all the food that the king liked best. Ahasuerus and Haman had a wonderful time, eating and drinking, but the king couldn't help noticing that Esther wasn't eating at all. In fact, she was crying.

'What's the matter?' he asked, with his mouth full. 'Why aren't you eating, my dear?'

'How can I eat,' replied Esther, 'when I'm going to die tomorrow along with all my family?'

'What!' said the king.

'I am a Jew,' explained Esther, 'and you said we should all die tomorrow. My father, Mordecai, all my brothers and sisters and cousins, and me, too, because I am a Jew'.

'Oh, this is dreadful,' said the king. 'I don't want to lose my lovely Queen. Whose idea was this?'

'It was Haman's idea,' said the queen.

'Well, I think it is Haman who should die tomorrow, then,' said Ahasuerus.

So Haman was hanged on the high gallows he had prepared for Mordecai. Esther and Mordecai asked the Jews to celebrate the festival of Purim for evermore.

1. Read what Judith and Joshua tell you about Purim.

Purim is a very special festival for Jewish children. We are allowed to come to the synagogue in fancy dress, and bring rattles and all sort of noisy things. Afterwards, we all eat special pastries called Haman's Ears.

When the rabbi reads the Megillah, the story of how Esther saved the Jews, we all have to listen carefully - for some names we say 'Hooray!' and for other names we say 'Boo!'

2. Colour 'Hooray!' or 'Boo!'

When we hear Queen Esther, we say …

When we hear Haman, we say …

When we hear Mordecai, we say …

Hooray!	Boo!
Hooray!	Boo!
Hooray!	Boo!

3. Complete the sentences.

At Purim we can wear _____

_____

We can eat _____

_____

I have eaten these special foods at festivals _____

_____

1. Design your own fancy dress to wear to the synagogue at Purim.

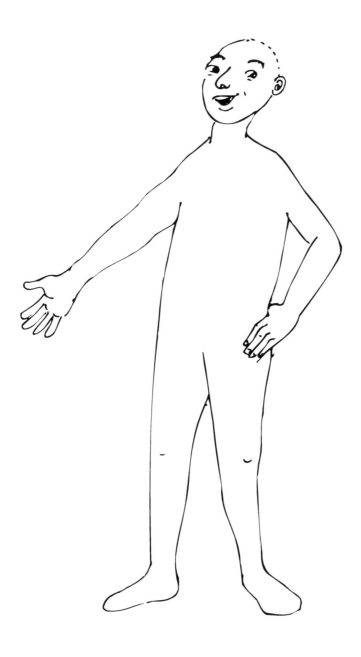

2. At Purim I would like to wear _____

_____

_____

_____

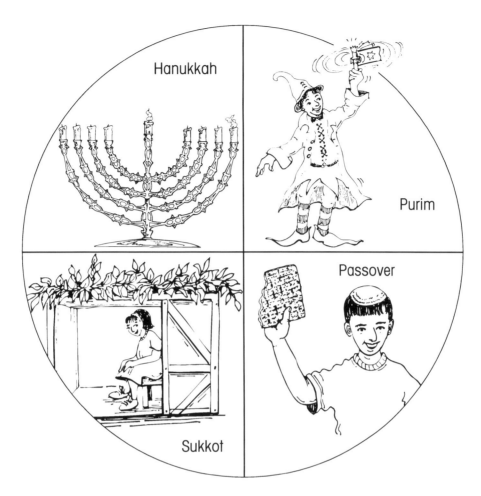

Use the words in the box to fill in the spaces.

Sukkot	**bread**	**Hanukkah**	**leaves**	**Purim**
Passover	**festivals**	**Esther**	**candles**	

Jewish children have lots of _____ during the year. In spring

they dress up for _____ to celebrate how Queen _____ saved

the Jews long ago. Then at _____ they eat special _____

made with no yeast to remind them how the Jews left Egypt in a hurry. In the

autumn they live under a special shelter made of branches and _____

for a week at _____. Then in the middle of winter they light their

_____ every night for _____ .

Teachers Notes

Religion: Judaism

Curriculum Links:

R.E. Attainment Target 1: Learning about Religions

- Practices and lifestyles - identify some religious practices and know that some are characteristic of more than one religion.

R.E. Attainment Target 2: Learning from Religion

- Identity and experience - identify aspects of own experience and feelings in religious materials studied.

QCA R.E. Scheme of Work Reference

- 2C - Celebrations.
- 1E - How do Jewish people express their beliefs?

National Literacy Strategy Reference

- Year 2, Term 2, Word 6 - read and spell words from *Appendix List 1,* (numbers to twenty).

Story Reference:

First and second Books of Maccabees, Apocrypha.

Notes – Page 40 – Strange Events in the Temple:

Introduction/Discussion:

- This story is not found in the Jewish Torah or Christian Bible but in the Apocrypha or additional books of the Greek Bible. The festival is a traditional celebration of the historical victory of Judah Maccabi over the Greek forces of Antiochus IV in Jerusalem in 165 BCE.

- Look at and read the frames with the children and discuss the events in each one:
    1. The Jews are chasing the Greek soldiers out of the Temple in Jerusalem. This was the most sacred place for the Jews.
    2. The Temple has been ransacked, the Greeks have placed statues of their gods in the holy places. The special Temple light that traditionally burns all the time has gone out and there is only a tiny quantity of oil for it.
    3. The Temple light is still burning even though there was so little oil.
    4. When fresh supplies of oil arrived after eight days, the tiny amount of oil was still burning. Jews saw this as a sign of God's pleasure in their victory.

Notes – Page 41 – A Story:

Introduction/Discussion:
- Remind the children of the main events in the story of Hanukkah.
- Brainstorm the vocabulary children will need.
- Provide a list of key phrases to help children structure a simple retelling of the story.

Resources:
- Pencil or pen.

Answers:
- Teacher check.

Notes – Page 42 – Lights:

Introduction/Discussion:
- Talk to the children about their own experience of lights used in religious contexts.
- Discuss which religion celebrates each festival and which lights they use.

Resources:
- Pencil or pen and crayons.

Answers:
- Easter - candle - Christian.
- Divali - Divali lamp - Hindu.
- Hanukkah - Hanukkah candlestick - Jew.
- Eid - crescent moon - Muslim.

Notes – Page 43 – Number Words:

Introduction/Discussion:
- Explain how Jewish families light candles every evening at Hanukkah to celebrate how God kept the Temple lamps burning for eight days.
- Show the children a Hanukkah candlestick (or a picture of one).
- Light the candles in sequence while you discuss the festival of Hanukkah. If you do not have a candlestick, use a row of nightlights on a metal tray.

Resources:
- Pencil or pen, Hanukkah candlestick (or picture of candlestick), candles and matches.

Answers:
1. one, two, three, four, five, six, seven, eight, nine.
2. ten, eleven, twelve, thirteen, fourteen, fifteen, sixteen, seventeen, eighteen, nineteen, twenty.

Strange Events in the Temple

A Story

Imagine your father went to get the oil. Tell him what happened at the temple while he was away for eight days.

Many religions use light as a symbol of the presence of God.

Draw different coloured lines to match these lights to the festival and faith that uses them.

EASTER

JUDAISM

DIVALI

CHRISTIANITY

HANUKKAH

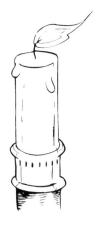

ISLAM

EID

HINDUISM

Jewish families light candles every year at Hanukkah to celebrate how God kept the Temple lamps burning for eight days.

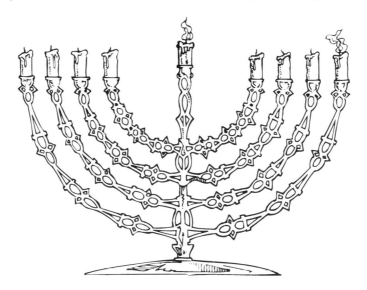

1.   Write the number words in the spaces.

On the 1st day of Hanukkah we burn _____ candle.

On the 2nd day of Hanukkah we burn _____ candles.

On the 3rd day of Hanukkah we burn _____ candles.

On the 4th day of Hanukkah we burn _____ candles.

On the 5th day of Hanukkah we burn _____ candles.

On the 6th day of Hanukkah we burn _____ candles.

On the 7th day of Hanukkah we burn _____ candles.

On the 8th day of Hanukkah we burn all _____ candles.

Altogether there are _____ candles. The 9th candle is called the
servant *and is used to light the other candles each night.*

2.   On the back of this sheet, write the number words for 10 – 20.

Teachers Notes

Religion: Hinduism

Curriculum Links:

R.E. Attainment Target 1: Learning about Religions

- Expression and language - suggest meanings in religious symbols, language and stories.

R.E. Attainment Target 2: Learning from Religion

- Meaning and purpose - realise that some questions that cause people to wonder are difficult to answer.

QCA R.E. Scheme of Work Reference

- 2C - Celebrations.
- 1D - Beliefs and practices.

National Literacy Strategy Reference

- Year 2, Term 2, Word 10 - words linked to particular topics.

Story Reference:

Traditional Hindu story retold in *Seasons of Splendour* by Madhur Jaffrey.

Seasonal Link:

The festival of Divali generally falls in October or November.

Notes – Page 46 – The Queen's Necklace:

Introduction/Discussion:

- Explain some of the traditions of Divali, how Hindu families will clean and decorate the house, then light tiny oil lamps called divas at dusk to welcome Lakshmi, the goddess of wealth and good fortune.
- Read the story with the children.
- Stop when the washerwoman leaves the palace and ask the children to predict how the story will end.
- Discuss the washerwoman's strategy.
- Did the king realise what would happen?
- Was it fair to the rest of the city?

Notes – Page 47 – The Queen's Necklace:

Introduction/Discussion:
- Brainstorm the sequence of events in the story.
- Look at the pictures with the children and discuss where each scene fits into the story.

Activity:
- Once children have coloured, cut out and sequenced pictures, get them to stick them in the correct order in a concertina book. Children could design their own front page. If space is available, more able children could retell the story by writing their own sentences underneath each picture.

Resources:
- Pencil or pen, crayons, scissors, glue and paper.

Answers:

Notes – Page 48 – The Washerwoman's Choice:

Introduction/Discussion:
- Read the story of The Queen's Necklace.
- Discuss the ending of the story.
- Ask children to consider the questions on the worksheet and brainstorm possible answers.
- Take a vote on what their choice would have been.

Resources:
- Pencil or pen and crayons.

Answers:
1. Lakshmi's blessing.
2–4. Teacher check.

Notes – Page 49 – Divali Wordsearch:

Introduction/Discussion:
- Discuss the illustrations - match them to the words.
- What do each of the words mean?

Resources:
- Pencil or pen, non-fiction books on Divali.

Answers:

f	i	r	e	w	o	r	k	s
m	g	a	r	l	a	n	d	w
e	s	n	x	b	z	g	q	e
n	a	g	t	e	m	p	l	e
d	r	o	d	i	v	a	w	t
h	i	l	i	g	h	t	s	s
i	m	i	t	a	r	s	e	m
d	a	n	c	i	n	g	p	o

The Queen's Necklace

Once upon a time, in India, there lived a king and queen. The queen loved fine jewels, so, one year, the king gave her a splendid new pearl necklace for Divali.

The next morning, the queen went to bathe in the river, leaving her new necklace on the river bank. Suddenly, a bird swooped down and flew off with it. The queen was very upset and said she would give a reward to anyone who found it.

The bird dropped the necklace on the doorstep of a poor washerwoman. As soon as the washerwoman saw it, she ran to the palace to show the king. He was delighted and offered her a huge bag full of gold.

To his surprise, the washerwoman replied, 'Your Majesty, you do not need to pay me anything for returning the queen's necklace to her. Instead, please grant me this humble favour. Tonight, let mine be the only lamps lit in this city'.

The king thought this was a very cheap way to reward the woman, so he promised to tell everyone to keep their houses dark that night.

On the way home the washerwoman bought all the oil lamps she could find, and arranged them in neat lines outside her poor hut. At dusk she lit them.

Each year, the goddess Lakshmi comes to earth ready to bless all the houses

where the Divali lights are burning. This year, everywhere was dark. The goddess could find no welcoming lights as she walked past the great houses and palaces of the city.

Then, down by the river where the poor people lived, Lakshmi saw one hut with bright twinkling lights outside. She knocked on the door and called, 'Let me in! Let me in! It is dark out here!'

'Only if you promise to stay here for my children and my grandchildren and my great-grandchildren and ...' answered the poor washerwoman.

'Yes, yes,' interrupted Lakshmi. 'I promise I'll stay for seven generations if you'll just let me in now.'

So the washerwoman opened the door of the hut to Lakshmi, and Lakshmi stayed and brought happiness and prosperity to her family for seven generations.

The Queen's Necklace

1. **Colour and cut out the pictures.**

2. **Glue the pictures in the correct order to tell the story.**

 RE and Literacy in the Classroom

The Washerwoman's Choice

1. Colour the correct answer.

The washerwoman chose:

A bag of money

Lakshmi's blessing

2. Colour the correct answer.

Do you think she was right?   Yes | No

3. What would you choose? _____

_____

_____

4. Why? _____

_____

_____

Divali Wordsearch

Find the hidden Divali words in the wordsearch.

f	i	r	e	w	o	r	k	s
m	g	a	r	l	a	n	d	w
e	s	n	x	b	z	g	q	e
n	a	g	t	e	m	p	l	e
d	r	o	d	i	v	a	w	t
h	i	l	i	g	h	t	s	s
i	m	i	t	a	r	s	e	m
d	a	n	c	i	n	g	p	o

Teachers Notes

Religion: Hinduism

Curriculum Links:

R.E. Attainment Target 1: Learning about Religions

- Beliefs and teachings - recount outlines of some religious stories.

R.E. Attainment Target 2: Learning from Religion

- Meaning and purpose - identify things they find interesting or puzzling in religious materials studied.

QCA R.E. Scheme of Work Reference

- 1D - Beliefs and practices.
- 2D - Visiting a place of worship.

National Literacy Strategy Reference

- Year 1, Term 2, Text 6 - story themes from traditional stories.

Story Reference:

This is a traditional Hindu story retold many times, including:
- *Out of the Ark* by Anita Ganeri (Simon and Schuster Young Books, 1994)
- *Seasons of Splendour* by Madhur Jaffrey (Pavilion, 1985)

Notes – Page 52 – The Story of Ganesh:

Introduction/Discussion:

- Show the children traditional images of some Hindu gods including Ganesh, either from a book or by visiting a temple.
- Read the story to the class, explaining that this popular story is told to explain why Ganesh is always shown with the body of a human child and the head of an elephant.

Notes – Page 53 – Parvati, Shiva and Ganesh:

Introduction/Discussion:

- Discuss the events in the story.
- Brainstorm the emotions felt by each character at key points in the story.
- Provide children with a list of words and phrases to use in their written work.

Resources:

- Pencil or pen and crayons.

Answers:

1. Answers should show awareness that Parvati was lonely because of Shiva's frequent absence from their home in the mountains.
2. Children should realise that Shiva wanted to see Parvati and was not aware that the child blocking his path was their son.
3. Children should explain that the elephant was the first living thing Shiva encountered after Parvati sent him to get a new head for Ganesh.

Notes – Page 54 – Elephants and other Animals:

Introduction/Discussion:

- Look at pictures of Ganesh and elephants from non-fiction books.
- Ask the children to think about all the information they know about elephants.
- Discuss which elephant qualities might also be appropriate for a god.
- Brainstorm words that might describe other animals; e.g. brave as a lion.

Resources:

- Pencil or pen, crayons and non-fiction books/pictures of Ganesh and elephants.

Answers:

1. Teacher check - answers could include: wisdom, strength, patience, large ears to hear everything, a large nose to smell everything, the ability to help people.
2. (a) brave (b) quiet   (c) greedy
   (d) free   (e) crafty   (f) vain
3. Teacher check.

Notes – Page 55 – Story Book Animals:

Introduction/Discussion:

- Show the children a collection of class books that have animal characters, including the six stories on the worksheet.
- Read the worksheet with the children, look at the pictures of animal characters and ask children to identify the story from which each comes.

Resources:

- Pencil or pen, crayons and collection of fiction books containing animal characters.

Answers:

1. (a) Goldilocks and the Three Bears   (b) The Frog Prince   (c) Jack and the Beanstalk
   (d) Billy Goats Gruff   (e) The Three Little Pigs   (f) Little Red Riding Hood
2. Teacher check.

The Hindu god Shiva and his wife Parvati lived high up in the Himalayan Mountains. Shiva was often away, so Parvati got bored and lonely.

One day, she decided to make herself a baby out of clay. She rolled the damp clay until it was shaped just like a fat little baby boy, then she breathed on him, to bring him to life. Parvati called her little boy Ganesh. Looking after Ganesh kept Parvati busy and happy, while she waited for Shiva to come home.

One hot day, a few years later, Parvati asked Ganesh to keep guard for her while she bathed in a mountain pool.

On that very day, Shiva came home. He heard his wife splashing and singing in the pool and went to join her, but a little boy he had never seen before stepped out and barred his way. Shiva was so angry he pulled out his sword and cut off Ganesh's head. When Parvati saw what Shiva had done she cried and cried.

'You killed our son!' she told Shiva.

'Go into the forest,' she ordered, 'and cut off the head of the first living thing you see. Give that head to our son and bring him back to life'.

Shiva ran into the forest and came back with an elephant's head. He fitted it onto Ganesh's lifeless body then breathed on him until he woke up.

When Parvati saw her fat little boy with his fine new head, huge ears and trunk, she loved him even more than she did before.

Complete the sentences and colour the pictures.

Parvati was lonely because

_____

_____

_____

_____

Shiva was angry because

_____

_____

_____

_____

Ganesh has an elephant head because

_____

_____

_____

_____

Elephants and other Animals

Hindus worship Ganesh as an elephant god because he is strong and wise like an elephant and good at moving obstacles from their path.

1. **List other words to describe an elephant.** _____

2. **Unjumble the words to find out what we say about these animals.**

   (a) As ___ ___ ___ ___ ___ as a lion. (ebavr)

   (b) As ___ ___ ___ ___ ___ as a mouse. (tqieu)

   (c) As ___ ___ ___ ___ ___ ___ as a pig. (eegdyr)

   (d) As ___ ___ ___ ___ as a bird. (efre)

   (e) As ___ ___ ___ ___ ___ ___ as a fox. (ftcyra)

   (f) As ___ ___ ___ ___ as a peacock. (nvia)

3. **Write words we use to describe other animals.**

Animal	Word
_____	_____
_____	_____
_____	_____

There are animals in lots of fairy stories.

1. Write the name of the story underneath the correct animal picture.

Jack and the Beanstalk	Goldilocks and the Three Bears	The Frog Prince
Little Red Riding Hood	Billy Goats Gruff	The Three Little Pigs

_____ _____ _____

_____ _____ _____

2. List other animal stories you have read on the back of this sheet.

Teachers Notes

Religion: Islam

Curriculum Links:

R.E. Attainment Target 1: Learning about Religions
• Beliefs and teachings - describe some religious beliefs and teachings of religions studied and their importance.
R.E. Attainment Target 2: Learning from Religion
• Values and commitments - make links between values and commitments, including religious ones, and their own attitudes or behaviour.
QCA R.E. Scheme of Work Reference
• 2D - Visiting a place of worship.
National Literacy Strategy Reference
• Year 2, Term 2, Word 10 - words linked to a particular topic.

Story Reference:

This story is found in various accounts of the life of Muhammad, including:
• *Stories from The Muslim World* by Huda Khattab (Ta-Ha, 1996)

Notes – Page 58 – The Story of Bilal:

Introduction/Discussion:

- Read the story with the children.
- Explain that there are no pictures of the people in the story because Muslims believe it is wrong to make representations of human beings, especially holy people like Muhammad and Bilal.
- What is a slave?
- Why was Umayya angry with Bilal?
- How did Abu Bakr save Bilal?
- What did Bilal do to help Muhammad?
- How do we know when to go to church or other religious services?

Notes – Page 59 – Bilal's Story:

Introduction/Discussion:

- Discuss the key events in the story of the first muezzin.
- Read the sentence starters on the worksheet and ensure children understand how these will help them structure their writing.
- Make a list of useful words and phrases for children to use in their own retelling of the story.

Resources:

- Pencil or pen and crayons.

Answers:

- Teacher check.

Notes – Page 60 – Bilal's Message:

Introduction/Discussion:

- Re-read the end of the story of the first muezzin with the children.
- On the board, copy the English version of the call to prayer that Bilal created.
- Discuss Bilal's message.
- Share ideas about what are the most important aspects of religious beliefs for other faiths, e.g. the Creed for Christians.
- In a single-faith school it may be appropriate to devise a shared message. Elsewhere teachers may prefer children to write their own simple statement of belief.

Resources:

- Pencil or pen and crayons.

Answers:

- Teacher check.

Notes – Page 61 – Visiting a Mosque:

Introduction/Discussion:

- This sheet could be used either before or after visiting a local mosque.
- If a mosque visit is not possible, non-fiction books may have illustrations showing the inside of a traditional mosque.
- Read the text with the children and try to identify each feature on the drawing.

Resources:

- Pencil or pen, crayons, glue and scissors.

Answers:

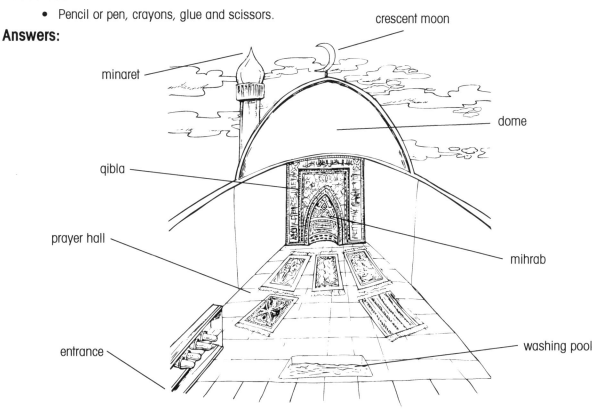

The Story of Bilal

Long ago in Mecca there was a slave called Bilal who had a beautiful voice. He heard Muhammad preaching in the marketplace and decided to become a Muslim.

His master, Umayya, was very angry, so he took Bilal out to the desert and made him lie on the hot sand with a rock on his chest, until he promised to worship idols again. Bilal grew very weak, but he still called out loudly, 'One God! There is only one God!'

When Bilal was almost dead of thirst, Abu Bakr, a rich Muslim, came by and found him. He was angry with Umayya for torturing Bilal because of his faith. Umayya refused to stop, so Abu Bakr bought Bilal the slave from his cruel master, took him back to Mecca and set him free.

Now Bilal was able to follow Muhammad and learn more about Islam. When Muhammad went to Medina, Bilal went too and helped to build a new mosque.

In those days, there were no clocks or watches, so it was hard for people to know when it was time to pray.

One night, one of Muhammad's friends dreamed that he had heard a loud, strong voice calling him to prayer. Muhammad realised God was telling them how to bring the people of Medina to the mosque. He chose Bilal because of his beautiful voice.

'What shall I say?' asked Bilal.

'Say what needs to be said,' replied Muhammad.

So Bilal climbed onto the mosque roof, put his hands either side of his mouth and called out all the most important things he had learned as a Muslim.

'God is Great. There is no God but Allah and Muhammad is his messenger. Come to prayer.'

Today, every mosque has a muezzin who climbs to the top of the minaret and gives the call to prayer, just as Bilal did so many years ago.

Retell the story of Bilal.

A long time ago lived a slave called Bilal. Bilal wanted	Bilal's master was angry, so he 
Bilal was rescued by	When Muhammad went to Medina
Bilal helped to build	Bilal climbed on the roof to 

Bilal called out the most important things he had learned as a Muslim.

1. **Write what you would say if you had to put all of the most important things that you believe into a few sentences.**

Mosques are often decorated with beautiful patterns, because Muslims believe it's wrong to make pictures of people or animals.

2. **Colour the pattern.**

Read and label how Muslims use the different parts of the mosque.

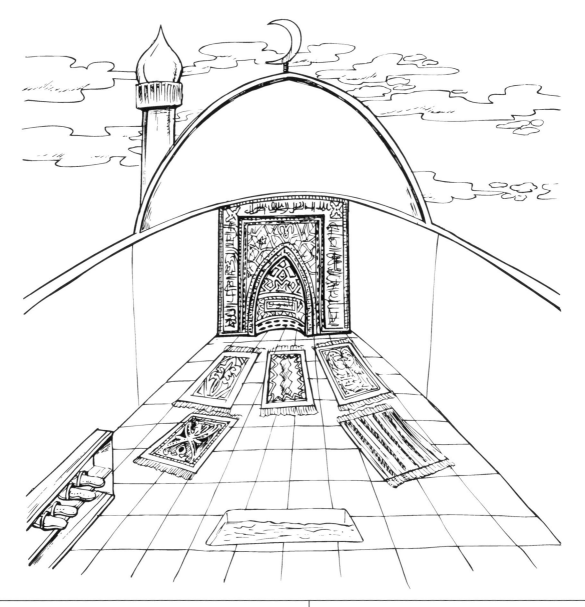

Before praying Muslims wash in the **washing pool** in the courtyard.	Muslims kneel on mats in the **prayer hall**.
At the **entrance** to the mosque, Muslims remove their shoes and place them on racks.	The muezzin climbs up to the **minaret** to give the call to prayer.
The **crescent moon** is a symbol of Islam.	The **mihrab** on the wall shows which way Muslims face for their prayers.
The **qibla** is the wall of the prayer hall that faces Mecca.	Many mosques have a **dome** on the roof.

Religion: Islam

Curriculum Links:

R.E. Attainment Target 1: Learning about Religions
• Beliefs and teachings - recount outlines of some religious stories.

R.E. Attainment Target 2: Learning from Religion
• Values and commitments - identify what is of value and concern to themselves in religious material studied.

QCA R.E. Scheme of Work Reference
• 1D - Beliefs and practice.

National Literacy Strategy Reference
• Year 1, Term 2, Word 2 - words ending in -ng.

Story Reference:

This is a traditional Muslim story and does not appear in the Biblical version of the life of King Solomon. It is retold in:
• *Out of the Ark* by Anita Ganeri (Simon and Schuster Young Books, 1994).

Notes – Page 64 – The Story of King Solomon and the Ants:

Introduction/Discussion:

- Discuss what the children already know about ants – how big they are, how they live in groups with a queen, etc.
- Read the story with the children.
- Explain any unfamiliar vocabulary.
- How did the queen know the ants were in danger?
- How did King Solomon save the ants?
- What makes King Solomon so special?
- What do we do when we see ants on the path?
- What does this story suggest we should do?

Notes – Page 65 – The Soldier's Story:

Introduction/Discussion:

- Remind the children of the main events in the story of King Solomon and the Ants.
- Drama - act out the story in the hall or playground. Choose two children to play Solomon and the Ant Queen. Then half of the class can be crawling on the floor as ants, while the other half march around the hall as Solomon's army. The Ant Queen gives her call of distress. Solomon hears her and orders his army to tiptoe. The soldiers then tiptoe safely around the ants to the other side of the hall. The children can then exchange roles.
- Ask the children to imagine how it felt to be soldiers tiptoeing around the ants.
- Brainstorm some suggestions with the class about how to record their experiences and how they will start and end the story.
- Put useful words on the board to support their writing.

Resources:

- Pencil or pen and crayons.

Answers:

• Teacher check.

Notes – Page 66 – Kindness to Animals:

Introduction/Discussion:
- This worksheet would be particularly appropriate for use after a class visit to a farm or animal park.
- Look at the worksheet with the children. Tell them a little bit about the teachings of St Francis, Buddha and Hinduism on how we should treat animals.

Resources:
- Pencil or pen and crayons.

Answers:
- Teacher check.

Notes – Page 67 – Rhyming Words:

Introduction/Discussion:
- Remind children of previous literacy work on word endings.
- Look at the pictures on the worksheet and discuss which word ending in *-ng* will match each picture.
- Encourage children to sound out the words and spell them independently.

Resources:
- Pencil or pen and crayons.

Answers:
1. (a) ring (b) wing (c) swing (d) sing (e) sting (f) string
2. Teacher check.

The Story of King Solomon and the Ants

Once upon a time there was a family of ants who lived in a quiet valley.

The ants worked all day long. Some of them went out looking for food, some of them looked after the new baby ants and some were always busy repairing the nest or building new rooms for their growing family.

Their queen ant was the mother of them all, and they loved her.

One day the ants heard a strange noise. It sounded like thunder, but the sky was blue. The noise seemed to be coming closer and closer. The ants were scared. They started to run away.

The queen came out to see what was the matter. She climbed right to the top of the nest and looked up. She saw an army of soldiers marching down the valley towards the ants' nest. At the head of the army rode a man on horseback. The noise that had frightened the ants was the sound of the soldiers'  feet and the horses' hooves crashing down onto the stony ground.

The queen could see that they were all in great danger. Her family of ants would all be crushed under those big feet.

'Run!' she shouted, in her little ant voice. 'Run to our nest as fast as you can or the soldiers will tread on you!'

Luckily for her, the man at the head of the army was no ordinary soldier, but King Solomon himself. King Solomon could speak and understand the languages of all the birds in the air, all the fish in the sea and all the animals in the world. He could hear the ant queen's voice clearly through all the noise of tramping feet.

'Don't worry, your Majesty!' he called to her. Then Solomon ordered his army to stop marching and to move more carefully so they did not step on any of the ant queen's family.

The ants watched while Solomon and his horses and his soldiers tiptoed through their valley. Not a single ant was hurt.

The ants always remembered King Solomon for his kindness.

This is one of the stories Muslims tell about how King Solomon could talk to animals.

Imagine you are one of King Solomon's soldiers. Write your version of the story.

Many religions ask us to be kind to animals.

1.   Read about some of these ways.

Saints like St Francis
teach Christians to take
care of animals.

Hindus treat cows
with great respect.

Buddhists respect all
life and eat no meat.

2.   List some ways we could be kind to animals.

_____

_____

_____

_____

_____

'King' ends with the letters –ng.

1.   Write these –ng words.

(a) (b)_____ _____ _____ _____ (c)

(d)_____ _____ _____ _____   (e)_____ _____ _____ _____   (f) _____ _____ _____ _____

2.   Write words that rhyme with each of these words.

queen    **nest**   **feet** 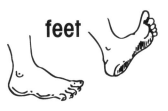   **hear**

_____   _____   _____   _____

_____   _____   _____   _____

_____   _____   _____   _____

Teachers Notes

Religion: Sikhism

Curriculum Links:

R.E. Attainment Target 1: Learning about Religions

- Beliefs and teachings - retell religious stories and identify some religious beliefs and teachings.

R.E. Attainment Target 2: Learning from Religion

- Values and commitments - respond sensitively to the values and concerns of others, including those with a faith, in relation to matters of right and wrong.

QCA R.E. Scheme of Work Reference

- 1D - Beliefs and practice.

National Literacy Strategy Reference

- Year 1, Term 3, Word 7 - spell common irregular words from Appendix List 1 (common colour words).

Story Reference:

A story about Guru Gobind Singh, retold in:
- *Stories from The Sikh World* by Rani and Jugnu Singh (Macdonald, 1987)

Notes – Page 70 – The Donkey and the Tiger Skin:

Introduction/Discussion:

- Read the story with the children.
- Explain that the Sikh gurus were teachers who often used stories to illustrate their message.
- How did the Guru feel about the donkey at the beginning of the story?
- Why did people treat the donkey differently the next day?
- What do tigers eat?
- Do tigers carry pots?
- What does the last sentence mean?

Notes – Page 71 – A Tiger or a Donkey?:

Introduction/Discussion:

- Ask the children to imagine living in the village where this story is set.
- How would they feel if they saw a donkey dropping things?
- How would they feel if a tiger was coming towards them?
- Suggest some appropriate words and phrases for recording these feelings.

Resources:

- Pencil or pen and crayons.

Answers:

- Teacher check.

Notes – Page 72 – How Do They Look?:

Introduction/Discussion:

- The class could begin this activity by dressing up in a variety of costumes and discussing what kind of person they represent when they try on each outfit.
- Discuss the significance of each set of clothes and what kind of person they would expect to see wearing each outfit.
- Brainstorm some useful words and phrases to help children complete the worksheet.
- Children colour the pictures and write a sentence about each. More able children could add more descriptive phrases to their sentences; e.g. I am a soldier and I march up and down.

Resources:

- Pencil or pen, crayons and collection of dressing-up clothes.

Answers:

- Teacher check.

Notes – Page 73 – A Market Stall:

Introduction/Discussion:

- Show pictures of a market stall and discuss children's experiences of shopping in a traditional market or the produce department of a supermarket.
- Ensure children can identify all fruits and vegetables listed before they begin to colour and label the stall.

Resources:

- Pencil or pen, crayons and pictures of market stalls.

Answers:

1. (a) green
   (b) yellow
   (c) brown
   (d) red
   (e) orange
2 – 4. Teacher check.

The Donkey and the Tiger Skin

Long ago, in India, Guru Gobind Singh was walking through a village when he saw the potter and his donkey carrying some new pots to market. The potter had loaded so many heavy clay pots onto the donkey's back that it could hardly walk. The pots kept falling off onto the road and breaking.

People were shouting and laughing and making fun of the poor donkey. The Guru felt sorry for the donkey and thought how different it would be if the donkey had been a tiger.

Next day he borrowed the potter's donkey and put a tiger skin rug onto its back. Then he took the donkey back to the market.

As soon as the people saw the tiger they screamed. Women picked up their babies and ran indoors. The men left their market stalls. Even the dogs barked and ran to hide.

The donkey was surprised, but very happy because the market stalls were full of lovely fruit and vegetables. Only the Guru was watching, and he smiled to see a tiger eating mangoes and carrots.

Then the donkey trotted off to the potter's workshop to find its master. When the man saw a tiger coming in he dropped the pot he was making and ran.

The frightened villagers decided to get together and chase the tiger away with some loud music. The donkey didn't like the noise so he ran into the forest. As the people followed him, banging drums and yelling, the donkey began to bray, 'Hee Haw! Hee Haw!'

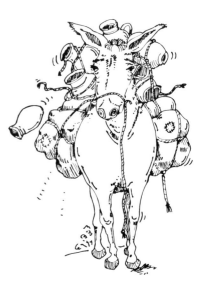

'That's a funny noise for a tiger,' said the villagers. Then the donkey tried to hide in a bush, and his tiger skin got caught on a branch and fell off.

'It's my donkey!' shouted the potter. Everyone smiled and patted the donkey. Then the donkey and his master went to collect some more pots for sale.

The Guru said, 'It is not enough to wear a tiger's clothes, you need to be as brave as the tiger'.

A Tiger or a Donkey?

When I saw the tiger

Complete the sentences.

When I saw the donkey

How Do They Look?

The Guru said it was not enough to look brave, the Sikhs must also behave bravely.

Write a sentence to explain what these clothes say about people.

A Market Stall

1. Unjumble the colour words.

(a) The melons are __ __ __ __ __. (rgene)

(b) The bananas are __ __ __ __ __ __ . (loylew)

(c) The coconuts and onions are __ __ __ __ __. (nbwro)

(d) The apples are __ __ __ . (dre)

(e) The carrots and oranges are __ __ __ __ __ __ . (eonrag)

2. Colour the fruit and vegetables correctly. Write their names.

3. My favourite fruit is _____

4. My favourite vegetable is _____

Religion: Buddhism

Curriculum Links:

R.E. Attainment Target 1: Learning about Religions

- Beliefs and teachings - recount outlines of some religious stories.

R.E. Attainment Target 2: Learning from Religion

- Meaning and purpose - identify things they find interesting or puzzling in religious materials studied.

QCA R.E. Scheme of Work Reference

- 1D - Beliefs and practice.

National Literacy Strategy Reference

- Year 1, Term 2, Word 10 - vocabulary extension linked to particular topics.

Story Reference:

This is a traditional Buddhist story retold in:
- *Out of the Ark* by Anita Ganeri (Simon and Schuster Young Books, 1994)

Notes – Page 76 – The Hare and the Earthquake:

Introduction/Discussion:

- Read the story with the children.
- Explain any unfamiliar vocabulary.
- What was Hare's biggest worry?
- Did Hare do the right thing when he ran through the forest shouting?
- What might have happened to the animals if they had not met Lion?
- What should Hare have done?

Notes – Page 77 – What did Hare Hear?:

Introduction/Discussion:

- Look at the picture with the children.
- Ensure that the children understand the difference between the noise Hare actually heard and what he thought he heard.

Resources:

- Pencil or pen and crayons.

Answers:

- Teacher check - answers should indicate that Hare only heard a fruit fall from the tree but thought he had heard an earthquake.

Notes – Page 78 – What Do You Do?:

Introduction/Discussion:

- Help children to appreciate how Hare's panic endangered all the other animals.
- Encourage the children to relate the story to issues in their own lives such as sharing, personal safety and taking responsibility for others.
- Discuss what we mean by trust and suggest some appropriate people familiar to the children who can be trusted.
- Make a list of useful words and phrases to help children formulate their personal response to each question.

Resources:

- Pencil or pen and crayons.

Answers:

1. Teacher check.
2. (a) yes (b) no (c) no
3. Teacher check.

Notes – Page 79 – Animal Movements:

Introduction/Discussion:

- Before doing this worksheet, children could watch animal movements either on video or during a visit to a zoo or park.
- The class could practise making different animal movements in a P.E. lesson, improvising from their knowledge of animals.
- Read the worksheet text with the children and then re-read the story, listening for movement words.

Resources:

- Pencil or pen and crayons.

Answers:

1. (a) Hares ran.   (b) Deer leapt.   (c) Buffalo stampeded.
   (d) Tigers streaked.   (e) Elephants thundered.

2. Teacher check - possible answers include:
   (a) Mice - creep, scuttle.   (b) Frogs - hop, jump.   (c) Snakes - slither, slide.
   (d) Horses - trot, gallop.   (e) Butterflies - flutter, glide (f) Monkeys - climb, swing.
3. Teacher check.

The Hare and the Earthquake

Once upon a time there was a hare who lived in a forest near the seaside. Hare used to worry about a lot of things. He used to worry that one day he would have no more green grass to eat. He used to worry that one day he would have no more fresh water to drink. Most of all, he used to worry that one day the world might fall apart in a great earthquake.

One day, Hare was dozing in the shade when a big ripe fruit fell to the ground right behind him. The noise made Hare jump. He was sure this meant the world was starting to fall apart. So he ran through the forest shouting to all the hares he met, 'Quick, run! It's an earthquake! The world is falling apart!'

Soon the hares were all running through the forest. The hares shouted to the deer, 'Quick, run! It's an earthquake!'

The deer all leapt through the forest and shouted to the buffalo,

'Quick, run! It's an earthquake!'

The buffalo all stampeded through the forest and shouted to the tigers,

'Quick, run! It's an earthquake!'

The tigers all streaked through the forest and shouted to the elephants,

'Quick, run! It's an earthquake!'

The elephants all thundered through the forest until they reached a beach.

Waiting for them on the beach was an enormous lion. He opened his mouth and gave a great roar. The animals stopped on the sand.

'Why are you running into the sea?' asked Lion. 'You'll all drown if you don't stop.'

'It's an earthquake!' panted the animals. 'The world is falling apart!'

'Really?' asked Lion. 'Who saw this earthquake start?'

'I did,' said Hare. 'I was sitting under the fruit trees when I heard such a loud bang. I knew it was the world starting to fall apart.'

'Show me,' said Lion.

So Hare rode on his back all the way to the fruit trees. Then Lion walked around the trees until he found the big ripe fruit on the ground. 'That was your earthquake,' he told Hare.

So Hare ran back happily to tell all the other animals not to be afraid.

Buddhists say that the lion was really Buddha who came to save the animals from the sea.

What did Hare Hear?

Complete the sentences.

Hare thought he heard

_____
_____
_____
_____
_____

Hare heard

_____
_____
_____
_____

What Do You Do?

The animals who listened to the hare and ran from the earthquake could all have drowned if Buddha had not appeared as a lion to stop them.

1. **What does this story teach us?** _____

    _____

2. **Complete the sentences.**

    (a) Your friends want to play football with your ball.

    You say _____

    (b) A stranger tells you to get into his or her car.

    You say _____

    (c) Your friend dares you to 'hide' someone's pencil.

    You say _____

3. **Draw and name four people you can trust. Here are some ideas.**

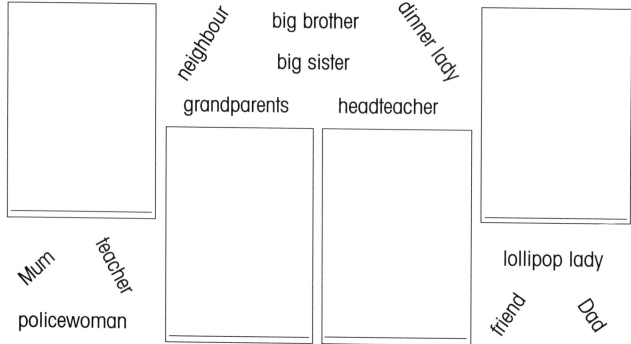

neighbour   big brother   dinner lady

big sister

grandparents   headteacher

Mum   teacher   lollipop lady

policewoman   friend   Dad

• 78 •

1. **Read the story to find the words used to describe how these animals moved through the forest.**

    (a) The hares __ __ __.

    (b) The deer __ __ __ __ __.

    (c) The buffalo __ __ __ __ __ __ __ __ __ __.

    (d) The tigers __ __ __ __ __ __ __ __ __.

    (e) The elephants __ __ __ __ __ __ __ __ __ __.

2. **Write words to describe how each animal moves.**

    (a) Mice _____

    (b) Frogs _____

    _____

    _____

    (c) Snakes _____

    (d) Horses _____

    _____

    _____

    _____

    _____

    (e) Butterflies _____

    (f) Monkeys _____

    _____

    _____

3. **Draw your favourite animal on the back of this sheet. Write how it moves.**